THE ULTIMATE
WASHINGTON FOOTBALL
TEAM TRIVIA BOOK

A Collection of Amazing Trivia Quizzes
and Fun Facts for Die-Hard Redskins Fans!

Ray Walker

Exclusive Free Book

Crazy Sports Stories

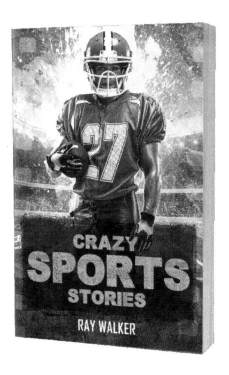

As a thank you for getting a copy of this book I would like to offer you a free copy of my book Crazy Sports Stories which comes packed with interesting stories from your favorite sports such as Football, Hockey, Baseball, Basketball and more.

Grab your free copy over at
RayWalkerMedia.com/Bonus

CONTENTS

INTRODUCTION

Team fandom should be inspirational. Our attachment to our favorite teams should fill us with pride, excitement, loyalty, and a sense of fulfillment in knowing that we are part of a community with many other fans who feel the same way.

Washington Football Team fans are no exception. With a rich, successful history in the NFL, the Football Team has inspired its supporters to strive for greatness with its tradition of colorful players, memorable eras, big moves, and unique moments.

This book is meant to be a celebration of those moments and an examination of the interesting, impressive, and important details that allow us to understand the full stories behind the players and the team.

You may use the book as you wish. Each chapter contains 20 quiz questions in a mixture of multiple-choice and true-false formats, an answer key (Don't worry, it's on a separate page!), and a section of 10 "Did You Know?" facts about the team.

Some will use it to test themselves with the quiz questions. How much Football Team history do you really know? How many of the finer points can you remember? Some will use it competitively (Isn't that the heart of sports?), waging contests with friends and fellow devotees to see who can lay claim to being the biggest fan. Some will enjoy it as a learning experience, gaining insight to enrich their fandom and add color to their understanding of their favorite team. Still others may use it to teach, sharing the wonderful anecdotes inside to inspire a new generation of fans to hop aboard the Washington bandwagon.

Whatever your purpose may be, we hope you enjoy delving into the amazing background of Football Team football!

Oh…and for the record, information and statistics in this book are current up to the beginning of 2021. The Football Team will surely topple more records and win more awards as the seasons pass, so keep this in mind when you're watching the next game with your friends, and someone starts a conversation with "Did you know…?".

CHAPTER 1:

ORIGINS & HISTORY

QUIZ TIME!

1. In which year did the franchise now known as the Washington Football Team begin playing in the National Football League?

   a. 1922
   b. 1932
   c. 1942
   d. 1952

2. The franchise was nearly called the Presidents, partially in homage to the city where the White House, the home of the nation's president, resides, and partially to honor a defunct rugby team from the city by that name.

   a. True
   b. False

3. How was the nickname "Redskins" initially chosen for the team when they were entering the NFL?

a. The team was originally founded as the Boston Braves but changed to the similarly themed name Redskins because a Major League Baseball team was already called the Boston Braves.

b. The original owner had a personal feud with Dallas Cowboys founder Clinton Murchison Jr. and chose the name to set up a "Cowboys-and-Indians-themed rivalry."

c. The franchise held a "Name the Team" contest sponsored by a local newspaper, and the winner was drawn in a lottery from a list of approved finalists.

d. The founder had Native American roots and wanted a nickname that would honor his heritage.

4. In which season did the Washington franchise begin to play in its new stadium, Jack Kent Cooke Stadium (now called FedEx Field), after moving from its longtime home at RFK Stadium?

   a. 1985
   b. 1992
   c. 1997
   d. 2003

5. Who was the founder of the team, when they were first known as the Boston Braves?

   a. Jack Kent Cooke
   b. b. Pete Rozelle
   c. c. George Stanley Halas
   d. d. George Preston Marshall

6. In which season did the Washington franchise earn its first playoff berth?

    a. 1932

    b. 1934

    c. 1936

    d. 1942

7. The Washington Football Team won more games than any other NFL team during the period between 1982 and 1992.

    a. True

    b. False

8. How many times in franchise history has the team won a division title?

    a. 10

    b. 15

    c. 20

    d. 25

9. During the team's first season in existence, who were the first franchise players ever to be named to the NFL All-Pro Team?

    a. Running back Cliff Battles, tackle Turk Edwards, and guard George Hurley

    b. Quarterback Dutch Clark, tackle Tom Nash, and center Mel Hein

    c. Running back Sammy Baugh, quarterback Riley Smith, and guard Ed Kahn

d. Center Frank Bausch, guard Les Olsson, and running back Ace Gutowsky

10. Which other NFL franchises is the Football Team tied with for winning three Super Bowl championships?

   a. New York Giants and Dallas Cowboys
   b. Green Bay Packers and Baltimore/Indianapolis Colts
   c. Denver Broncos and Los Angeles/Oakland/Las Vegas Raiders
   d. Kansas City Chiefs and Miami Dolphins

11. How did the franchise fare during its 50th anniversary season in the NFL?

   a. Missed the playoffs altogether
   b. Lost in the first round to the Green Bay Packers
   c. Lost in the NFC Championship to the Dallas Cowboys
   d. Won the Super Bowl over the Miami Dolphins

12. The longest stretch the team has gone without making the playoffs was a 25-year drought, from 1946 to 1970.

   a. True
   b. False

13. Which team did the franchise face in its very first NFL game (which resulted in a 21-6 loss)?

   a. Chicago Bears
   b. New York Giants
   c. St. Louis Gunners
   d. Brooklyn Dodgers

14. What were the details surrounding the franchise's first NFL game?

    a. They lost to the Chicago Bears, 21-7.
    b. They won over the Pittsburgh Pirates, 10-3.
    c. They were shut out by the Brooklyn Dodgers, 14-0.
    d. They shutout the Portsmouth Spartans, 7-0.

15. When the franchise was first admitted to the NFL, it replaced which of the following franchises that had left the league?

    a. Staten Island Stapletons
    b. Frankford Yellow Jackets
    c. Providence Steam Roller
    d. Cleveland Indians

16. As of 2021, Washington is tied with the New York Giants and Pittsburgh Steelers as the franchise that has sent more players to the Pro Bowl than any other NFL franchise.

    a. True
    b. False

17. How did Washington fare in its first NFL playoff run?

    a. Lost in the first round to the Portsmouth Spartans
    b. Lost in the first round to the Brooklyn Dodgers
    c. Lost the NFL championship to the Green Bay Packers
    d. Won the NFL championship against the Chicago Bears

18. What is Washington's franchise record for most victories recorded by the club in a single regular season?

a. 15

b. 14

c. 13

d. 12

19. What is the name of the Football Team mascot?

a. Chief Touchdown

b. Running Bear

c. Washington Wally

d. The Football Team does not have a mascot.

20. The Washington football franchise has, at some point, been included in both the Western Conference and the Eastern Conference.

a. True

b. False

QUIZ ANSWERS

1. B – 1932

2. B – False

3. A – The team was originally founded as the Boston Braves but changed to the similarly themed name Redskins because a Major League Baseball team was already called the Boston Braves.

4. C – 1997

5. D – George Preston Marshall

6. C – 1936

7. B – False

8. B – 15

9. A – Running back Cliff Battles, tackle Turk Edwards, and guard George Hurley

10. C – Denver Broncos and Los Angeles/Oakland/Las Vegas Raiders

11. D – Won the Super Bowl over the Miami Dolphins

12. A – True

13. D – Brooklyn Dodgers

14. C – They were shut out by the Brooklyn Dodgers, 14-0.

15. D – Cleveland Indians

16. B – False

17. C – Lost the NFL championship to the Green Bay Packers

18. B – 14

19. D – The Football Team does not have a mascot.

20. B – False

DID YOU KNOW?

1. Technically, the Football Team has played at five different home stadiums during its existence. Most people are aware of FedEx Field, RFK Stadium, and Griffith Stadium, each of which housed the team for decades. But the franchise also played one year at Braves Field and for four seasons at Fenway Park.

2. The worst win-loss record ever logged by the Washington Football Team came in 1961 when the team won only a single game and finished the season 1-12-1.

3. FedEx Field, the current home of the Football Team, is actually located in Landover, Maryland, while the team's headquarters is in an entirely different state. Those offices and the Football Team's training facility are situated in Ashburn, Virginia.

4. While the Football Team is an anchor tenant of FedEx Field, that is not their home exclusively. No other team plays its full schedule there because it is dedicated mainly for NFL use, but the stadium has occasionally hosted college football and international soccer matches throughout its existence.

5. From 1961 to 1966, the Football Team played its home games at Robert F. Kennedy Stadium in Washington, D.C. This multipurpose venue housed not just the Washington

Redskins, but also many other Washington teams, such as the NCAA Colonials, MLB Senators and Nationals, NASL Whips and Diplomats, USFL Federals, and MLS DC United.

6. As a new team entering the NFL in 1932, the franchise did not have to pay a single dollar as a fee for the right to join the league; the owners simply had to be willing to pay the operating expenses. For context, when the Houston Texans joined in 2002, they paid an expansion fee of $700 million.

7. Washington's biggest NFL rival is generally thought to be the Dallas Cowboys, and the rivalry has been considered by many as the top one in the NFL. The Cowboys have the advantage in the head-to-head rivalry at 73 wins, 45 losses, but the Football Team is undefeated (2-0) against Dallas in the playoffs.

8. At the first home game in franchise history, while the team still played in Boston, tickets for bleacher seats against the Brooklyn Dodgers sold for just 55 cents apiece. A spot in the grandstands cost $1.10, and box seats went for $1.65.

9. In 1937, Washington formed the Washington Redskins Marching Band, becoming the first team in the NFL to have its own official band. The band most often performed the team's official fight song (also a first of its kind), "Hail to the Redskins."

10. During the Football Team's (then Boston Braves') first season in the NFL, 1932, ties did not count in the standings. This led to some anomalies because the Braves' tie games, including a 0-0 game against the New York Giants, were removed from their record, and the team finished 4-4. In contrast, the Green Bay Packers' record of 10-3 reflected five more games played.

CHAPTER 2:

JERSEYS & NUMBERS

QUIZ TIME!

1. When they began playing in the NFL in 1932, the Football Team used what color scheme for its home and away uniforms?

   a. Blue, white, and light brown
   b. Burgundy and gold
   c. Black, silver, and white
   d. Red and yellow

2. The numbers 0 and 00 have been banned from circulation by Washington owner Dan Snyder because they are seen to represent a losing attitude.

   a. True
   b. False

3. When the franchise gave up the "Redskins" nickname in 2020, what did it decide to use as its primary logo?

   a. The interlinking letters WFT
   b. A burgundy and gold football

c. The letter W

d. A pentagon shape with a football in the middle

4. Two excellent Washington wide receivers each wore number 82 for years with the team. Who were these two pass catchers?

   a. Gary Clark and Pierre Garcon

   b. Antwaan Randle El and Michael Westbrook

   c. Ricky Sanders and Hugh Taylor

   d. Art Monk and Terry McLaurin

5. In which year was approval received for player names to appear on the backs of Football Team jerseys?

   a. 1950

   b. 1960

   c. 1970

   d. 1980

6. Which uniform number has proven to be most popular with Football Team fans in 2011, having sold the most Washington jerseys on NFL.com?

   a. Wide receiver Santana Moss's number 89

   b. Quarterback Rex Grossman's number 8

   c. Defensive end Ryan Kerrigan's number 91

   d. Linebacker Brian Orakpo's number 98

7. The white jerseys worn by Washington are often said to have been "jinxed," and therefore, the team avoids wearing them during the Super Bowl whenever the choice is theirs.

   a. True

   b. False

8. Which of the following players chose to wear the highest-numbered jersey in Football Team franchise history?

    a. Defensive tackle Cornelius Griffin, number 96
    b. Linebacker Brian Orakpo, number 98
    c. Halfback and defensive back Eddie Saenz, number 99
    d. Running back Clinton Portis, number 100

9. The current version of the Football Team uniform includes three colors. Which of the following is NOT included in the color scheme?

    a. Burgundy
    b. Black
    c. White
    d. Gold

10. Fullback Johnny Olszewski is the only Football Team player ever to wear which of the following uniform numbers?

    a. 00
    b. 0
    c. 4
    d. 62

11. Sixteen players have worn number 11 for the Football Team. Which of them scored the most career touchdowns?

    a. Quarterback Mark Rypien
    b. Wide receiver DeSean Jackson
    c. Quarterback Patrick Ramsey
    d. Quarterback Alex Smith

12. Halfback Swede Ellstrom wore number 18 for the franchise in 1934 and remains the only member of the team to do so because his number was retired.

   a. True
   b. False

13. Why did star wide receiver Terry McLaurin choose to wear number 17 for Washington?

   a. In college with the Ohio State Buckeyes, he wore number 83, and decided to add 17 to that in the NFL to reflect his goal of racking up 100 receiving yards in every game.
   b. There were 17 wide receivers chosen ahead of him in the NFL Draft, and McLaurin wanted to motivate himself to become better than every one of them.
   c. It was chosen as a tribute to his older brother Gerald, who had passed away at age 17 when McLaurin was 12.
   d. It is a version of his birthdate, January 7, with 1 representing the month and 7 representing the day.

14. How many jersey numbers has the Washington Football Team retired for its former players?

   a. 1
   b. 2
   c. 5
   d. 7

15. Which player competed for the Football Team for just six seasons, the shortest tenure of anyone whose number has been retired by the franchise?

    a. Halfback and flanker Bobby Mitchell
    b. Tailback and quarterback Sammy Baugh
    c. Safety Sean Taylor
    d. Wide receiver Art Monk

16. Six players have worn the number 1 for Washington, and every single one of them was a quarterback.

    a. True
    b. False

17. Lucky number 7 has been worn by just two Football Team players over the years. Which athlete wore it for the longest time?

    a. Quarterback Dwayne Haskins
    b. Quarterback Mark Rypien
    c. Running back John Riggins
    d. Quarterback Joe Theismann

18. Who is the most recent Football Team player to have his number retired by the club?

    a. Quarterback Sammy Baugh
    b. Safety Sean Taylor
    c. Offensive tackle Joe Jacoby
    d. Running back Bobby Mitchell

19. Which number did star running back John Riggins, who was named Super Bowl MVP for the Football Team in 1983, wear on the back of his jersey?

a. 33

b. 39

c. 44

d. 48

20. The Washington Football Team has retired more jersey numbers than any other NFL franchise has.

a. True

b. False

QUIZ ANSWERS

1. A – Blue, white, and light brown

2. B – False

3. C – The letter W

4. B – Antwaan Randle El and Michael Westbrook

5. C – 1970

6. D – Linebacker Brian Orakpo's number 98

7. B – False

8. C – Halfback and defensive back Eddie Saenz, number 99

9. B – Black

10. B – 0

11. D – Quarterback Alex Smith

12. B – False

13. A – In college with the Ohio State Buckeyes, he wore number 83, and decided to add 17 to that in the NFL to reflect his goal of racking up 100 receiving yards in every game.

14. B – 2

15. A – Halfback and flanker Bobby Mitchell

16. B – False

17. D – Quarterback Joe Theismann

18. D – Running back Bobby Mitchell

19. C – 44

20. B – False

DID YOU KNOW?

1. In the 1960s, Washington, then known as the Redskins, decided to feature a spear with a feather attached on the sides of their helmet. The "spear helmet" was revered by fans and was later brought back by the team as part of a throwback uniform.

2. Eight numbers are not officially retired by the Washington Football Team but have not been worn by anyone since the player who made the number famous stopped playing. They are Sonny Jorgensen (9), Sean Taylor (21), Darrell Green (28), Charley Taylor (42), Larry Brown (43), John Riggins (44), Dave Butz (65), and Art Monk (81).

3. Defensive end Chase Young changed his number drastically when he was drafted by the Washington Football Team. In college at Ohio State, Young wore number 2, but shifted all the way up to number 99 with Washington to comply with NFL positional rules.

4. For the 2000 NFL season, Washington altered its jerseys not just in appearance, but also in performance design. Rather than the loose-fitting sleeves of the past, the team used an elastic material around the cuffs that not only looked sleeker but also prevented opponents from getting a grip on the jerseys to slow the players down.

5. Before the team removed the name and imagery associated with the name "Redskins" in 2020, the last major change to

the franchise uniforms was in 1971, when Washington settled on the profile of a Native American surrounded by feathers as its main logo.

6. After star quarterback Joe Theismann suffered a gruesome injury in 1985, no Washington player wore his number 7 for almost 35 years. Quarterback Dwayne Haskins took the hallowed number in 2019 but did not do it much credit because he was cut from the team after just a couple of seasons.

7. Superstition may have scared some Football Team players away from wearing the number 13. Only 14 players in franchise history have chosen it for themselves, and eight of them only wore it for a single season.

8. Since 1973, the NFL has not allowed players to wear 0 and 00. Only one player wore each number for Washington before this change occurred. Halfback and defensive back Steve Bagarus wore 00 in 1945, 1946, and 1948, and running back Johnny Olszewski wore 0 from 1958 to 1960.

9. The highest number ever retired by the Washington Football Team is number 49, belonging to halfback and flanker Bobby Mitchell. The team wore a patch with this number on it in 2020 to honor Mitchell after he passed away that year.

10. Football Team defensive lineman Jonathan Allen wore number 93 with Washington because he was a fan of defensive end Julius Peppers. As a high school player, Allen was under the mistaken impression that Peppers

wore number 93 (Peppers actually wore numbers 90 and 56 during his career).

CHAPTER 3:

CATCHY NICKNAMES

QUIZ TIME!

1. By which franchise nickname was the Washington Football Team most commonly referred to when they were officially called the Redskins?

    a. "The Tribe"
    b. "The Natives"
    c. "The 'Skins"
    d. "The Scalpers"

2. Hall of Fame Washington cornerback Darrell Green was often referred to as "The Flash" thanks to his incredible speed (Four times, he was declared the NFL's fastest man.), which gave him the ability to close on balls targeted to wide receivers who appeared open when the pass was thrown.

    a. True
    b. False

3. The longtime home of the Football Team, Robert F. Kennedy Stadium was also more colloquially known by which popular nickname?

    a. "The Ref"
    b. "The Kennedy Center"
    c. "The Tribal Lands"
    d. "The Bobby Bowl"

4. Which television show inspired the nickname given to Washington Football Team quarterback Kirk Cousins, "Captain Kirk"?

    a. Growing Pains
    b. Lifestyles of the Rich and Famous
    c. Star Trek
    d. Wheel of Fortune

5. Why was Football Team tight end Chris Cooley given the nickname "Captain Chaos" by his teammates?

    a. He created havoc against defenders by yelling nonsense signals and making meaningless gestures at the line of scrimmage.
    b. He was always running late and would pop into meetings at the very last second, scrambling to take his seat before coaches spoke.
    c. He won a bet with his teammates that he would not introduce himself as "Captain Chaos" to opponents during the coin toss before a game.
    d. He wore an amalgam of superhero accessories to a team Halloween party, including Superman's cape,

an oversized ring similar to the Green Lantern's, and Captain America's shield.

6. Which of the following is NOT a position group that Lorenzo Alexander played on during his time with the Football Team, leading to his nickname as the "One-Man Gang"?

   a. Tight end
   b. Defensive line
   c. Defensive back
   d. Offensive line

7. Washington safety Sean Taylor was known as "Meast" because as a fearsome hitter he was considered half man, half beast on the field.

   a. True
   b. False

8. Why was Washington running back Adrian Peterson given the nickname "All Day" by his parents?

   a. He would nag them incessantly about taking him to the local football field to play with other kids.
   b. He refused to quit playing new video games and step away from the television until he had beaten every single level.
   c. He preferred to stay up throughout the night and sleep all day.
   d. He had so much energy that he did not stop running all day long.

9. Which teammate did quirky Football Team running back Clinton Portis refer to as "Johnny White Guy" during a press conference?

    a. Quarterback Kirk Cousins

    b. Defensive end Ryan Kerrigan

    c. Quarterback Mark Brunell

    d. Tight end Chris Cooley

10. Powerful Football Team running back John Riggins went by which one-word nickname?

    a. "Tank"

    b. "Diesel"

    c. "Punisher"

    d. "Smash"

11. What was large Football Team defensive tackle Dan Wilkinson affectionately known as to fans and teammates, because of his 6'5", 340-pound body?

    a. "Big Daddy"

    b. "Two Ton"

    c. "Mega Man"

    d. "The Pizza Hut"

12. After engaging in two memorable fights with his former Washington teammates as a newly traded member of the New York Jets, ex-Football Team wide receiver Laveranues Coles earned the nickname "The Vengeful Ex."

    a. True

    b. False

13. In the 1970s, Washington's team was dubbed the "Over the Hill Gang." Why was this moniker bestowed upon them?

   a. They were the group of teammates who finally ended Washington's decades-long playoff drought, getting the team "over the hill."

   b. Several Caucasian team leaders had participated in civil rights marches to Capitol Hill, in solidarity with the team's African-American players.

   c. They collected so many older, veteran players that the team's average age rose to 31 years old.

   d. The team had cut failed 1st overall draft pick, quarterback Jerry Hill, in 1969 and made a fresh start despite the embarrassment of blowing the pick.

14. Most NFL fans actually knew Washington quarterback Sammy Baugh very well by which alliterative nickname that celebrated his enjoyment of the forward pass?

   a. "Bombs Away Baugh"
   b. "Strong Arm Sammy"
   c. "Big Play Baugh"
   d. "Slingin' Sammy"

15. Which of the following is NOT a real superfan (or group of superfans) of the Washington Football Team known for attending games in character?

   a. "Chief Zee," the team's unofficial mascot, who wore a headdress and brought a tomahawk

b. "El Presidente," who wore an Uncle Sam costume with stripes in the team colors instead of red, white, and blue

c. "The Hogettes," who revered the team's offensive line while dressed in drag and fake pig snouts

d. "SuperSkin," who sported a gold and burgundy superhero costume at every home game

16. Washington quarterback Alex Smith was called "The Professor" by his young teammates because he was brought in to provide leadership and playoff experience while demonstrating how to act like a professional athlete.

    a. True
    b. False

17. FedEx Field, the current home of the Football Team, was built on a site known by which of the following nicknames (inspired by a combination of the owner's sons' first names)?

    a. "Jabob" (from Jack and Robert)
    b. "Stemark" (from Steven and Mark)
    c. "Raljon" (from Ralph and John)
    d. "Regway" (from Reginald and Wayne)

18. Who coined the term "The Hogs" for Washington's talented offensive line group in the 1980s and 1990s?

    a. Offensive line coach for Washington Joe Bugel
    b. Sportswriter for the *Washington Post* Michael Wilbon
    c. Linebacker for the New York Giants Lawrence Taylor
    d. Analyst for *Monday Night Football* Howard Cosell

19. "The Posse" was a talented group of wide receivers that starred for Washington, amassed over 1,000 receiving yards each during a single season, and included which three players?

    a. DeSean Jackson, Santana Moss, and Ricky Proehl
    b. Hugh Taylor, Charley Taylor, and Jerry Smith
    c. Ricky Sanders, Art Monk, and Gary Clark
    d. Terry McLaurin, Antonio Gandy-Golden, and Steven Sims Jr.

20. Washington guard Mark Schlereth was given the nickname "Stink" in large part due to his unusual practice of urinating in full uniform whenever he felt the need to go, even if that was during a game or while he was on the bench.

    a. True
    b. False

QUIZ ANSWERS

1. C – "The 'Skins"

2. B – False

3. A – "The Ref"

4. C – *Star Trek*

5. C – He won a bet with his teammates that he would not introduce himself as "Captain Chaos" to opponents during the coin toss before a game.

6. C – Defensive back

7. A – True

8. D – He had so much energy that he did not stop running all day long.

9. D – Tight end Chris Cooley

10. B – "Diesel"

11. A – "Big Daddy"

12. B – False

13. C – They collected so many older, veteran players that the team's average age rose to 31 years old.

14. D – "Slingin' Sammy"

15. B – "El Presidente," who wore an Uncle Sam costume with stripes in the team colors instead of red, white, and blue

16. B – False

17. C – "Raljon" (from Ralph and John)

18. A – Offensive line coach for Washington Joe Bugel

19. C – Ricky Sanders, Art Monk, and Gary Clark

20. A – True

DID YOU KNOW?

1. A talented group of Washington offensive players helped to inspire the NFL's alter-ego as the "No Fun League." Seven Football Team members in the early 1980s celebrated touchdowns in the end zone together and became known as "The Fun Bunch." Eventually, the league cracked down on these choreographed routines and began penalizing players who continued to celebrate excessively.

2. Football Team defensive end and top overall pick Chase Young earned the nickname "Predator," partially for his intensity and skill level when rushing the passer and partially because his dreadlock hairstyle looks like the characters from the *Predator* movie franchise.

3. Before much mainstream controversy arose surrounding the use of the nickname "Redskins," two colleges used to use this name as well (Miami University of Ohio and Southern Nazarene University). This meant that, when Washington selected quarterback Bruce Matte from Miami in the 1967 NFL Draft, Matte's team nickname did not change upon joining the NFL.

4. During the 1980s and 1990s, Washington's offensive line was widely revered for controlling the line of scrimmage as one of the biggest and most powerful collections of talent in NFL history. Though the pieces changed over the years, this group, nicknamed "The Hogs," primarily

consisted of Mark May, Jeff Bostic, Joe Jacoby, Russ Grimm, and George Starke.

5. There is a section of the NFL rulebook known as "the Baugh/Marshall Rule" after Washington quarterback Sammy Baugh and owner George Preston Marshall. The rule states that a passed ball is dead if it hits the goalposts. Marshall fought to get this rule enacted after a Baugh pass did so, resulting in the game-winning safety for the Cleveland Rams in the 1945 NFL Championship Game.

6. Darrell Green, who represented Washington on the NFL's 100th Anniversary All-Time Team, played 20 years in the NFL and retired at age 42. For this longevity, Green earned the nickname "Ageless Wonder" toward the end of his career.

7. While "The Posse" made the most headlines for Washington during the 1980s, another wide receiver trio also contributed to the team's success. Known as "The Smurfs," this diminutive group consisted of 5'7" Alvin Garrett, 5'8" Virgil Seay, and 5'10" Charlie Brown.

8. Cornerback Deion Sanders joined the Football Team with two nicknames. "Neon Deion" referred to his flashy personality and style of play. "Prime Time" was chosen because he made people tune in to watch him, as they would for popular television shows aired in the evening.

9. Because of the team's poor results under Washington owner Daniel Snyder, the franchise was often referred to

by both fans and rivals as "The Deadskins" during the 2000s.

10. After the Football Team collected a quartet of talented defensive linemen and assembled them in 2020, the team's defensive line became known as "The Department of Defense." This nickname played off a similarly named government department hosted in Washington and included players Chase Young, Montez Sweat, Daron Payne, and Jonathan Allen.

CHAPTER 4:

THE QUARTERBACKS

QUIZ TIME!

1. Which of these Football Team quarterbacks has been sacked by opponents the most times during his career (340 times sacked)?

   a. Billy Kilmer
   b. Kirk Cousins
   c. Joe Theismann
   d. Robert Griffin III

2. Sonny Jurgensen holds the top four spots on the Football Team all-time list of most passing touchdowns thrown in a season?

   a. True
   b. False

3. Which quarterback has thrown the most interceptions in franchise history?

   a. Mark Rypien
   b. Eddie LeBaron

    c. Joe Theismann

    d. Sammy Baugh

4. Who is the Washington Football Team's all-time career leader in passing yards?

    a. Joe Theismann

    b. Sonny Jurgensen

    c. Sammy Baugh

    d. Kirk Cousins

5. Who set the franchise record for most passing yards in a season by a Washington quarterback?

    a. Mark Rypien

    b. Jay Schroeder

    c. Kirk Cousins

    d. Joe Theismann

6. How many former quarterbacks for the Football Team have been elected to the Pro Football Hall of Fame?

    a. Sammy Baugh

    b. Sammy Baugh and Sonny Jurgensen

    c. Sammy Baugh, Sonny Jurgensen, Doug Williams, and Joe Theismann

    d. Sammy Baugh, Sonny Jurgensen, Doug Williams, Joe Theismann, Billy Kilmer, and Eddie LeBaron

7. Incredibly, Sammy Baugh and Joe Theismann have played more games at quarterback for the Football Team than any other players, and each finished with exactly 167 contests.

a. True

b. False

8. One journeyman Football Team quarterback has played for 13 NFL teams, more than any other franchise leader. Who was this well-traveled player?

a. Case Keenum

b. Jeff George

c. Mark Rypien

d. Josh Johnson

9. Which Football Team passer was the youngest player in the team's history to start at quarterback, at just 21 years old?

a. Robert Griffin III

b. Ted Wright

c. Norm Snead

d. Dwayne Haskins

10. Which Washington quarterback was moved to the Oakland Raiders for a 4th round pick to make way for new quarterback Donovan McNabb after the Football Team acquired the superstar from the Philadelphia Eagles in 2010?

a. Jason Campbell

b. Rex Grossman

c. Mark Brunell

d. Robert Griffin III

11. Washington legend Sammy Baugh still holds which NFL record that is unusual for a quarterback to hold?

   a. Most consecutive long snaps without a turnover, with 307 snaps
   b. Longest field goal ever attempted, with a 76-yard attempt
   c. Most career interceptions *caught*, with 88 interceptions
   d. Longest yards per punt in a season, with 51.4 yards

12. Football Team quarterback Alex Smith named previous quarterback Kirk Cousins as the godfather when his daughter Sloane was born in 2017.

   a. True
   b. False

13. After suffering a gruesome leg injury in 1985, Football Team quarterback Joe Theismann retired and moved on to all of the following careers except for which one?

   a. Television analyst for ESPN and NFL Network broadcasts
   b. Assistant coach for his alma mater, the Notre Dame Fighting Irish
   c. Owner of a restaurant and bar
   d. Motivational speaker at corporate events

14. In which city did Washington quarterback Kirk Cousins set his career-high mark for passing yards in a single game, with 458?

   a. Cincinnati, Ohio
   b. Washington, D.C.

c. Minneapolis, Minnesota

d. London, England

15. Which of the following facts about Washington quarterback Doug Williams's performance in Super Bowl XXII is NOT true?

a. He was so nervous before the game that he vomited on the sidelines, which was caught on camera and shown on the television broadcast.

b. He underwent a six-hour root canal procedure the day before the big game.

c. He threw four touchdowns in the game, setting a Super Bowl record because all four came in the second quarter.

d. He became the first African-American quarterback to be victorious in the championship game and win the MVP award.

16. Washington quarterback Mark Rypien has won both a College Football National Championship and an NFL Super Bowl championship.

a. True

b. False

17. Which three-word phrase did Football Team quarterback Kirk Cousins famously yell to reporters after a 2015 game, leading to a trademark application and T-shirts bearing the phrase being sold for charity?

a. "Trust me, baby!"

b. "Stone-cold victory!"

c. "You like that?!"

d. "Yep, never again!"

18. Which of the following football connections related to star Washington quarterback Mark Rypien is NOT a real one?

   a. Rypien's nephew Brett became a quarterback in the NFL as well, for the Denver Broncos.

   b. Rypien finished his playing career as a Rochester Raider in the Great Lakes Indoor Football League.

   c. Rypien's daughter Angela competed for the Seattle Mist of the Lingerie Football League.

   d. Rypien's son Matthew was a running back for the XFL St. Louis Battlehawks.

19. How many times has a Football Team quarterback thrown for 30 (or more) passing touchdowns in a single season?

   a. 0

   b. 1

   c. 8

   d. 14

20. Among quarterbacks who have started at least five games with Washington, Ralph Guglielmi has the highest interception percentage, with 12.4% of his passes thrown being picked off.

   a. True

   b. False

QUIZ ANSWERS

1. C – Joe Theismann

2. B – False

3. D – Sammy Baugh

4. A – Joe Theismann

5. C – Kirk Cousins

6. B – 2: Sammy Baugh and Sonny Jurgensen

7. A – True

8. D – Josh Johnson

9. B – Ted Wright

10. A – Jason Campbell

11. D – Longest yards per punt in a season, with 51.4 yards

12. B – False

13. B – Assistant coach for his alma mater, the Notre Dame Fighting Irish

14. D – London, England

15. A – He was so nervous before the game that he vomited on the sidelines, which was caught on camera and shown on the television broadcast.

16. B – False

17. C – "You like that?!"

18. D – Rypien's son Matthew was a running back for the XFL St. Louis Battlehawks.

19. B – 1

20. A – True

DID YOU KNOW?

1. The longest possible passing play in the NFL is 99 yards. Washington was the first franchise to complete a play that long and is also the only team to have accomplished the feat more than once. In 1939, Frank Filchock threw a short pass that Andy Farkas took all the way to the end zone. In 1963, George Izzo launched a bomb that Bobby Mitchell hauled in near midfield before scoring. And, in 1968, Sonny Jurgensen hit Jerry Allen for the third 99-yard scoring play.

2. Only one Football Team quarterback has ever completed 70% of his passes in a season. This accurate field general was Sammy Baugh, who cracked this barrier in 1945, when he hit 70.3%.

3. Trent Green could have used some better blocking when he became the Washington quarterback in 1998. He was sacked a whopping 49 times, the highest total in Football Team history.

4. One Football Team quarterback played his entire NFL career with Washington. Sammy Baugh spent 16 seasons with the franchise, putting him just one season behind the current record holders (Dan Marino with the Miami Dolphins, John Brodie with the San Francisco 49ers, and two quarterbacks who are still active, Ben Roethlisberger

of the Pittsburgh Steelers and Aaron Rodgers of the Green Bay Packers).

5. Hall of Fame quarterback Sammy Baugh served the longest tenure as Washington quarterback. Baugh began his time with the team in 1937 and stayed until his retirement in 1952.

6. In 2009, former Washington quarterback Doug Williams partnered with former Bills, Rams, and Chargers quarterback James Harris to form the Black College Football Hall of Fame. Harris and Williams had both been stars at Grambling State University, a historically black university that later named a street in Williams's honor.

7. Washington quarterback Kirk Cousins was given the franchise tag by the Football Team in 2016 and again in 2017, making him the first quarterback in the NFL to receive the tag in back-to-back seasons. This gave Cousins incredible leverage in 2018, when he left Washington to sign the first fully guaranteed contract in NFL history, for three years and $84 million with the Minnesota Vikings.

8. Quarterback Alex Smith, a former 1st overall draft choice, was in his first year with Washington when he suffered a terrible leg injury during a game against the Houston Texans. Smith needed 17 surgeries to save his leg from amputation, and his life was in danger at several points due to sepsis, but he battled back to eventually return to the playing field.

9. Heath Shuler, who played quarterback for the Football Team in the 1990s, was perhaps more well-known even after his NFL career ended. Shuler started a large real estate company in Tennessee, then joined the Republican Party and became a congressman in North Carolina for several years.

10. For four seasons at the beginning of the 1970s, Washington was the scene of an ongoing quarterback controversy. Sonny Jurgensen and Billy Kilmer both vied to be the starter, with Kilmer getting the bulk of the opportunities. Though the two players were friendly, fans took sides by wearing buttons that said either "I Like Billy" or "I Like Sonny."

CHAPTER 5:

THE PASS CATCHERS

QUIZ TIME!

1. Five wide receivers have recorded over 50 career touchdown catches for the Football Team. Which one has the most?

   a. Hugh Taylor
   b. Charley Taylor
   c. Art Monk
   d. Gary Clark

2. No one in Football Team history is within 200 receptions of Art Monk at the top of Washington's record book.

   a. True
   b. False

3. Four pass catchers are tied atop the Football Team's single-season leaderboard in receiving touchdowns scored, with 12. Which four players share this mark?

   a. Bobby Mitchell, Santana Moss, Michael Westbrook, and Charlie Brown

b. Art Monk, Rod Gardner, Albert Connell, and Jamison Crowder

c. Gary Clark, Laveranues Coles, Pierre Garcon, and Terry McLaurin

d. Ricky Sanders, Charley Taylor, Hugh Taylor, and Jerry Smith

4. Who holds the all-time career franchise record for receiving yardage for the Football Team?

a. Art Monk

b. Santana Moss

c. Bobby Mitchell

d. Gary Clark

5. After his career ended, longtime star Football Team wide receiver Art Monk sued which two entities for failure to properly protect him from "the long-term brain injury risks associated with football-related concussions"?

a. The Washington Football Team and its team doctor, Joseph Wilson

b. Washington head coaches Joe Gibbs and Norv Turner

c. The NFL and helmet manufacturer Riddell Inc.

d. The NCAA and the NFL

6. Two Football Team players with at least 100 receptions have averaged over 19 yards per catch during their Washington careers. Which two have shown this amazing big play ability?

a. Henry Ellard and Albert Connell

b. Bill Anderson and Leslie Shepherd

c. Gary Clark and Michael Westbrook

d. Hugh Taylor and DeSean Jackson

7. Washington wide receiver Roy Jefferson was a teammate of his cousin in high school and college, but the two actually faced off against each other in the Super Bowl during their days in the NFL.

a. True

b. False

8. Which Football Team receiver has played more NFL games with the franchise than any other player?

a. Gary Clark

b. James Thrash

c. Art Monk

d. Ricky Sanders

9. Three pass catchers have over 550 career receptions for the Washington Football Team. Which of the following players is NOT among them?

a. Art Monk

b. Jordan Reed

c. Santana Moss

d. Charley Taylor

10. Despite all his accomplishments, Charley Taylor has more career fumbles than any other Washington wide receiver. How many times did he cough up the ball?

a. 18

b. 24

c. 28

d. 31

11. At the end of the 2020 NFL season, the Football Team had 11 wide receivers under contract. How many of those wide receivers averaged over $1 million a year in salary?

    a. 0

    b. 3

    c. 6

    d. 11

12. Hall of Fame electee and Super Bowl champion Football Team wide receiver Art Monk is a first cousin of equally renowned jazz pianist Thelonious Monk, who has won both a Pulitzer Prize and a Grammy Lifetime Achievement Award.

    a. True

    b. False

13. How many of the Football Team's tight ends have caught over 300 passes for the club during their careers?

    a. 1: Chris Cooley

    b. 2: Chris Cooley and Jerry Smith

    c. 3: Chris Cooley, Jerry Smith, and Jordan Reed

    d. 4: Chris Cooley, Jerry Smith, Jordan Reed, and Don Warren

14. Which two teammates posted the highest combined receiving yardage total in a season for the Football Team, with 2,415 yards?

a. Gary Clark and Art Monk in 1989

b. Ricky Sanders and Art Monk in 1990

c. DeSean Jackson and Pierre Garcon in 2016

d. Gary Clark and Art Monk in 1991

15. In which unusual way did excitable Football Team receiver Gary Clark occasionally celebrate Washington touchdowns?

a. Climbing onto a horse that usually rode with a team flag on the sidelines

b. Chugging Gatorade directly from the cooler without using a cup

c. Jogging laps around the stadium

d. Blowing kisses to the fans in the upper deck

16. In 1971, Washington employed a 6'11" wide receiver named Edward Robertson who played only on snaps involving a Hail Mary pass. Robertson used his height to come down with four touchdowns on the last play of a half or a game that season but was injured the following year in training camp and never played again.

a. True

b. False

17. Which of the following football achievements was NOT recorded by superstar Washington wide receiver Art Monk?

a. Becoming the first NFL player to catch a touchdown pass in 15 consecutive seasons

b. Having the highest number (14) of consecutive catches from his quarterback without another player catching a ball

c. Notching a record-long streak of 183 consecutive games with at least one reception

d. Earning the longest-lasting standing ovation of any Pro Football Hall of Fame member at his induction ceremony

18. Which Football Team player recorded the most catches in one season for the team, with 113?

a. Bobby Mitchell in 1962

b. Art Monk in 1984

c. Pierre Garcon in 2013

d. Terry McLaurin in 2020

19. In 1966, two teammates posted the highest touchdown reception total in a season for the Football Team, converting 21 passes into scores. Another two teammates matched the record the following year. Charley Taylor was one of the two each year; he accomplished this with which two different teammates?

a. Bobby Mitchell and Jerry Smith

b. A.D. Whitfield and Joe Don Looney

c. John Burrell and Steve Thurlow

d. Pat Richter and Bob Long

20. Football Team wide receiver Bobby Mitchell once held indoor world records in track and nearly shunned football for a chance to participate in the Summer Olympics but

was persuaded to join the NFL instead by a large payment from legendary coach Paul Brown.

a. True
b. False

QUIZ ANSWERS

1. B – Charley Taylor

2. A – True

3. D – Ricky Sanders, Charley Taylor, Hugh Taylor, and Jerry Smith

4. A – Art Monk

5. C – The NFL and helmet manufacturer Riddell Inc.

6. D – Hugh Taylor and DeSean Jackson

7. A – True

8. C – Art Monk

9. B – Jordan Reed

10. D – 31

11. A – 0

12. A – True

13. C – 3: Chris Cooley, Jerry Smith, and Jordan Reed

14. A – Gary Clark and Art Monk in 1989

15. C – Jogging laps around the stadium

16. B – False

17. B – Having the highest number (14) of consecutive catches from his quarterback without another player catching a ball

18. C – Pierre Garcon in 2013

19. A – Bobby Mitchell and Jerry Smith

20. A – True

DID YOU KNOW?

1. Washington icon Art Monk ranks 20th on the all-time list for most receptions in the NFL. When Monk retired in 1995, he was first on the list but has since been eclipsed by 19 players in an era that encourages more passing.

2. The single-game record for most receptions in Washington Football Team history was actually set by a running back. Roy Helu reeled in 14 passes against the San Francisco 49ers in 2011, passing four players who had been tied at the top with 13 catches.

3. Although he caught many key passes from quarterback Doug Williams, including nine in Super Bowl XXII, Washington receiver Ricky Sanders's most memorable catch may have come after the game. The team visited the White House, where U.S. President Ronald Reagan tossed a ceremonial pass that Sanders caught.

4. One of the best receivers in Washington history nearly didn't play for the team. The Football Team was the last NFL franchise to integrate, holding out until 1962 when Bobby Mitchell was one of three black athletes to join the squad. Mitchell made quite an impression, starting with a 92-yard kick return against the Dallas Cowboys in his first game for the team. He led the NFL in catches and receiving yards that season.

5. Talented tight end Jordan Reed made many Football Team fans wonder what could have been. Reed was very skilled but also highly injury-prone, and he missed over 40 games during his career, which included no fewer than seven diagnosed concussions.

6. Washington Pro Bowl wide receiver Santana Moss came from a very athletic family. His brother Sinorice Moss also played in the NFL, as a wide receiver mostly with the New York Giants, and his cousin Patrick Peterson became an eight-time Pro Bowl cornerback for the Arizona Cardinals.

7. Versatile Football Team player Charley Taylor could do it all. After being drafted as a running back and winning the Rookie of the Year Award at that position, Taylor moved to wide receiver the following season and promptly led the league in receiving yards the next two seasons. Upon his retirement, Taylor was the NFL's all-time leading receiver.

8. Washington wideout Michael Westbrook was known for his temper and once got fined $50,000 for throwing a punch at running back Stephen Davis, his teammate. In retirement, Westbrook channeled his anger and became a mixed martial artist, earning a professional record of one win, one loss, and one no contest.

9. Football Team tight end Jerry Smith was widely known as a top player of his era. He retired in 1978 with the most touchdown catches by a tight end in NFL history. What

many did not know was that Smith was one of the NFL's few gay players at the time. He kept this secret even after he retired, and the fact only came out after his death in 1986.

10. Washington wide receiver Henry Ellard was a strong enough athlete that he qualified for the 1992 Summer Olympic trials in the triple jump event. Due to a leg injury, Ellard did not get the chance to compete for a medal.

CHAPTER 6:

RUNNING WILD

QUIZ TIME!

1. Who holds the Football Team's single-season franchise rushing yardage record, with 1,613 yards?

   a. Clinton Portis
   b. Stephen Davis
   c. Terry Allen
   d. Alfred Morris

2. It is a Football Team tradition for every running back to tap his helmet against the helmets of the starting offensive linemen following the pre-game warm-up.

   a. True
   b. False

3. Which running back accumulated the most carries for Washington without ever scoring a rushing touchdown?

   a. Moses Denson
   b. Calvin Hill

c. Samaje Perine

d. Dale Atkeson

4. Which of the following is NOT a fact about quirky Football Team running back Clinton Portis?

a. He once admitted in a *Sports Illustrated* article that he had considered murdering his financial managers after they'd driven him to the verge of bankruptcy.

b. During the opening of training camp in 2008, Portis arrived via a hot air balloon that descended onto FedEx Field.

c. At age 21, against the Kansas City Chiefs, he was the youngest player in NFL history to score four touchdowns in a single game.

d. At age 22, against the Kansas City Chiefs, he was the youngest player in NFL history to score five touchdowns in a single game.

5. How many running backs have carried the ball over 1,000 times for the Football Team?

a. 2

b. 3

c. 6

d. 10

6. No Football Team running back with at least 16 games played has averaged over 100 yards per game during his career. Clinton Portis is the closest; what was his average?

a. 75.3 yards per game

b. 81.2 yards per game

c. 92.4 yards per game

d. 98.8 yards per game

7. John Riggins has 79 rushing touchdowns with the Football Team, which is more than the next three highest Washington running backs combined.

a. True

b. False

8. In which season did scrambling quarterback Robert Griffin III record an astonishing 6.8 yards per carry for Washington?

a. 2010

b. 2011

c. 2012

d. 2013

9. Which Washington running back (with at least 300 carries) has the highest career yards gained per attempt, with 5.8?

a. Max Krause

b. John Riggins

c. Alfred Morris

d. Stephen Davis

10. Running back Antonio Gibson recorded his first NFL touchdown for Washington against which NFL team?

a. Los Angeles Chargers

b. Dallas Cowboys

c. Green Bay Packers

d. Arizona Cardinals

11. How many of the Football Team's top 10 seasons for rushing touchdowns were recorded by the great John Riggins?

    a. 0
    b. 3
    c. 5
    d. 7

12. Before becoming an NFL star, Washington running back John Riggins majored in journalism at the University of Kansas and considered becoming a sports journalist.

    a. True
    b. False

13. Which Washington running back has the most career fumbles?

    a. Stephen Davis
    b. John Riggins
    c. Larry Brown
    d. Mike Thomas

14. Which Football Team player (with at least 250 carries) had the highest single-season rushing yards per game, with 101.3?

    a. Alfred Morris
    b. Frank Akins
    c. Terry Allen
    d. Larry Brown

15. The humble Alfred Morris may have been the Football Team's leading rusher for several years, but, in 2012, he still clung to the vehicle he'd driven before making it big. Which model was this?

    a. 1987 Toyota Tercel
    b. 1991 Mazda 626
    c. 1994 Ford Explorer
    d. 1997 Honda Accord

16. Washington running back Adrian Peterson finished as runner-up for college football's Heisman Trophy. This would not be unusual, except that Peterson was so good, he accomplished this feat in his *freshman* season, the first collegiate player ever to do so.

    a. True
    b. False

17. In a play voted by fans as the Washington Football Team's greatest moment, powerful running back John Riggins stiff-armed which Miami Dolphins cornerback on fourth down and inches, getting clear for a 43-yard touchdown that clinched a Super Bowl victory?

    a. Curtis Johnson
    b. Tim Foley
    c. Paul Lankford
    d. Don McNeal

18. After a stellar career that included a Super Bowl win in Washington, Football Team rusher Earnest Byner became

the team's running back coach. He went on to hold the same position for all of the following teams except which one?

a. Tampa Bay Buccaneers
b. Jacksonville Jaguars
c. St. Louis Rams
d. Tennessee Titans

19. Which of the following is NOT an NFL record held by ageless Football Team running back John Riggins?

a. Oldest player to score three rushing touchdowns in a single game (36 years old)
b. Most games with 100 yards rushing at age 35 or older (eight games)
c. Most number of games with at least 20 rushes at age 30 or older (36 games)
d. Oldest non-kicking player to start a Super Bowl game (35 years old)

20. In 2019, Football Team running back Adrian Peterson won the NFL's Art Rooney Award for demonstrating "the qualities of on-field sportsmanship, including fair play, respect for the game and opponents, and integrity in competition," which is voted on by fellow players.

a. True
b. False

QUIZ ANSWERS

1. D – Alfred Morris

2. B – False

3. A – Moses Denson

4. B – During the opening of training camp in 2008, Portis arrived via a hot air balloon that descended onto FedEx Field.

5. C – 6

6. B – 81.2 yards per game

7. B – False

8. C – 2012

9. A – Max Krause

10. D – Arizona Cardinals

11. B – 3

12. A – True

13. C – Larry Brown

14. D – Larry Brown

15. B – 1991 Mazda 626

16. A – True

17. D – Don McNeal

18. C – St. Louis Rams

19. D – Oldest non-kicking player to start a Super Bowl game (35 years old)

20. A – True

DID YOU KNOW?

1. Three running backs who played for the Football Team have been enshrined in the Pro Football Hall of Fame. The most recent was John Riggins, who was elected in 1992.

2. Washington running back Calvin Hill won the 1969 NFL Rookie of the Year Award, but he is not the most acclaimed athlete in his family. His son, Grant Hill, won the 1995 NBA Rookie of the Year Award and is an inductee of the Basketball Hall of Fame.

3. After three years as a backup to Terry Allen, Washington running back Stephen Davis got a chance to start in 1999 and made the most of it. Davis finished with 1,405 yards rushing and 17 touchdowns, scoring more points than any other non-kicker in the league. Davis easily made the Pro Bowl that year.

4. Washington running back John Riggins held out for the entire 1980 NFL season in a contract dispute with the team. In 1981, the confident Riggins told new head coach Joe Gibbs, "You need to get me back there. I'll make you famous." Gibbs helped sign Riggins to a new contract, and they became famous together.

5. The first NFL player to crack 200 yards rushing in a single game was Football Team halfback Cliff Battles. In 1933, Battles went off for 215 yards against the New York

Giants. Battles had signed with the Football Team instead of New York because they had offered $175 per game rather than the Giants' top offer of $150.

6. Star Football Team running back George Rogers has not one but two roads named in his honor. George Rogers Boulevard passes by Williams-Brice Stadium at Rogers's alma mater, the University of South Carolina, and Rogers's hometown, Duluth, Georgia, dedicated George Rogers Avenue in 2017.

7. During his tenure with Washington, legendary running back Adrian Peterson moved into the NFL's top 10 in all-time rushing yards. Peterson passed such greats as Jim Brown, Eric Dickerson, Jerome Bettis, LaDainian Tomlinson, and Curtis Martin to slide into fifth place in history.

8. Despite suiting up at running back for only five games with Washington and spending time before and after his Football Team stint with other franchises, Tim Hightower was highly thought of in Washington. In 2020, he was hired as the team's director of alumni relations.

9. Ten times in NFL history, a running back has scored 20 or more touchdowns in a single season. Two Football Team rushers have accomplished the feat: John Riggins had 24 in 1983, and Terry Allen had 21 in 1986. No other franchise has had two running backs achieve this mark.

10. Following his Hall of Fame football career, Washington running back John Riggins went into the acting business. In addition to appearing in an off-Broadway Shakespeare

play, Riggins landed roles on popular shows *One Tree Hill, Guiding Light,* and *Law & Order: Criminal Intent.*

CHAPTER 7:

IN THE TRENCHES

QUIZ TIME!

1. Five Football Team defenders have recorded four sacks in a single game. Which one did it most recently?

   a. Defensive end Chase Young
   b. Linebacker Brian Orakpo
   c. Defensive end Phillip Daniels
   d. Linebacker Ryan Kerrigan

2. The 2016 Washington Football Team holds the NFL record for the heaviest combined weight of all starting offensive and defensive linemen.

   a. True
   b. False

3. Who is the Football Team's all-time franchise leader in sacks, with 95.5?

   a. Linebacker Ryan Kerrigan
   b. Defensive end Dexter Manley

c. Defensive end Charles Mann

d. Defensive tackle Dave Butz

4. Which offensive lineman did the Football Team select highest in the NFL Entry Draft, using a 3rd overall choice to add the stout blocker to their team?

   a. Trent Williams in 2010

   b. I.B. Hale in 1939

   c. Brandon Scherff in 2015

   d. Chris Samuels in 2000

5. Which offensive lineman has played more games (196) on the offensive side of the Football Team line of scrimmage than anyone else?

   a. Center Len Hauss

   b. Left tackle Joe Jacoby

   c. Center Jeff Bostic

   d. Guard Ethan Albright

6. Which defensive lineman has played more games (203) on the defensive side of the Football Team's line of scrimmage than anyone else?

   a. Defensive end Charles Mann

   b. Defensive tackle Kedrick Golston

   c. Defensive tackle Dave Butz

   d. Defensive end Ron McDole

7. Longtime Football Team offensive lineman George Starke was cut by Washington during his first training camp. Luckily for the team, he was also cut by the Kansas City

Chiefs and Dallas Cowboys before returning to Washington and making the squad the following year.

a. True

b. False

8. Which Football Team defender showed the best nose for the ball by leading the team in career forced fumbles, with 26?

a. Wilber Marshall

b. Marcus Washington

c. London Fletcher

d. Ryan Kerrigan

9. Quarterbacks top the record books for most fumbles recovered for the Football Team, but they tend to be cleaning up their own mess. Which defender has created the most turnovers for Washington by scooping up an opponent's fumble 17 times?

a. Linebacker Brad Dusek

b. Defensive end John Paluck

c. Linebacker Chris Hanburger

d. Defensive tackle Darryl Grant

10. When Washington guard Mark May, a member of the famed "Hogs," wrote *Mark May's Hog Cookbook* in 1983, all of the following recipes were included except which one?

a. "Aunt Jeannette's Sweet Potato Pie"

b. "Hog Balls"

c. "Flattened Cowboy Pancakes"

d. "Hog Quiche"

11. Football Team mainstay left tackle Joe Jacoby played 170 NFL games with the club. Where does he rank in games played all-time for Washington?

    a. 1st overall
    b. 3rd overall
    c. 7th overall
    d. 10th overall

12. NFL umpire Roy Ellison was once suspended for a game after swearing at Washington offensive tackle Trent Williams during a previous contest.

    a. True
    b. False

13. Which current Football Team defensive lineman has the longest tenure in Washington?

    a. Ryan Kerrigan
    b. Daron Payne
    c. Montez Sweat
    d. Jonathan Allen

14. Which of the following facts about Football Team offensive lineman Chris Samuels is NOT true?

    a. He appeared on the cover of *Sports Illustrated* magazine.
    b. He coached under the legendary Nick Saban at the University of Alabama.
    c. He played every game of his NFL career for Washington.

d. He was named to a team-record eight consecutive Pro Bowls.

15. Football Team defensive end Charles Mann was highly respected throughout the NFL and in the Washington community for his humanitarianism. Mann even landed corporate spokesman positions with all of the following companies except which one?

a. McDonald's
b. Swanson
c. Diet Coke
d. Nike

16. Hall of Fame defensive end Bruce Smith played four years with the Football Team, notching his 200th quarterback sack while with the franchise in 2003 to break the legendary Reggie White's NFL record.

a. True
b. False

17. What ended star defensive end Dexter Manley's NFL career in 1991?

a. He broke his leg when a teammate accidentally rolled over it during practice.
b. He showed up to camp 40 pounds overweight and was beaten out by Charles Mann.
c. He failed four drug tests and decided not to appeal the resulting suspension.

d. He received a higher contract offer from the Canadian Football League's Ottawa Rough Riders and switched leagues.

18. Which of the following is NOT a fact about Washington defensive tackle Dave Butz?

    a. He was a board member of the National Rifle Association.
    b. He became a free agent in 1975 because of an error made in his rookie contract.
    c. He surfed in the offseason and participated in charity Pro-Am events.
    d. He was 38 years old when he retired, the oldest starter in the league at the time.

19. Which of the Football Team's famous "Hogs" on the offensive line went on to become a sideline reporter for the NFL on Westwood One?

    a. Tackle Joe Jacoby
    b. Guard Russ Grimm
    c. Guard Mark May
    d. Center Jeff Bostic

20. Washington guard and center Raleigh McKenzie had a twin brother named Reggie. Both McKenzie brothers played linebacker together in high school and college before Raleigh switched to the offensive line.

    a. True
    b. False

QUIZ ANSWERS

1. D – Linebacker Ryan Kerrigan

2. B – False

3. A – Linebacker Ryan Kerrigan

4. D – Chris Samuels in 2000

5. A – Center Len Hauss

6. C – Defensive tackle Dave Butz

7. A – True

8. D – Ryan Kerrigan

9. C – Linebacker Chris Hanburger

10. C – "Flattened Cowboy Pancakes"

11. D – 10th overall

12. A – True

13. A – Ryan Kerrigan

14. D – He was named to a team-record eight consecutive Pro Bowls.

15. D – Nike

16. A – True

17. C – He failed four drug tests and decided not to appeal the resulting suspension.

18. C – He surfed in the offseason and participated in charity Pro-Am events.

19. D – Center Jeff Bostic

20. A – True

DID YOU KNOW?

1. Willie Wilkin holds the Washington record for most safeties created, with two. Although he was an offensive lineman, Wilkin played on special teams and also recorded a touchdown on a blocked punt.

2. Defensive linemen Charles Mann and Tim Johnson joined teammates Art Monk and Earnest Byner to create the Good Samaritan Foundation, which provides high school students with tutoring, mentoring, and other necessary resources to help them be successful in life.

3. Washington Football Team sack specialist Bruce Smith was so good that he belongs to several elite establishments, including the Hampton Roads Sports Hall of Fame, Virginia Tech Sports Hall of Fame, the Virginia Hall of Fame, College Football Hall of Fame, and Pro Football Hall of Fame.

4. As the oldest of the group, offensive lineman George Starke was considered the "Head Hog" of the Football Team's "Hogs" line. Starke later opened two locations of Head Hog BBQ restaurants in Maryland.

5. Washington's "Hogs" performed well together off the field as well. The members each put up $500 to form the Super Hogs corporation, which sold "Hogs"-themed clothes, beer, posters, and other merchandise.

6. Football Team center and long snapper Ethan Albright briefly became famous in 2006, when he was rated as the worst player in the league in the popular video game *Madden NFL 07*. Albright was given a 53 on a 1-99 scale but had the last laugh when he became a Pro Bowler in 2007.

7. Center and guard Russ Grimm spent his entire decade-long playing career with Washington, and in retirement, he became an offensive line coach with four different franchises: Washington, the Pittsburgh Steelers, the Arizona Cardinals, and the Tennessee Titans.

8. Darryl Grant was drafted as an offensive guard in 1981, but Washington converted him into a defensive tackle, where he was a mainstay for several years.

9. Stalwart franchise left tackle Chris Samuels suffered a scary injury in 2019 when his entire upper body was temporarily paralyzed after a helmet-to-helmet collision during a game against the Carolina Panthers. Samuels retired without playing another game due to the danger of aggravating the injury if he returned.

10. Offensive tackle Trent Williams is known as "Silverback," as in a type of gorilla. He sports a gorilla tattoo and other assorted gorilla-based art pieces. Williams was even introduced by that nickname by NFL commissioner Roger Goodell when Washington drafted him in 2010.

CHAPTER 8:

THE BACK SEVEN

QUIZ TIME!

1. Which Football Team cornerback is the franchise's all-time leader in interceptions, with 54?

   a. DeAngelo Hall
   b. Deion Sanders
   c. Darrell Green
   d. Champ Bailey

2. During the 2010s poker craze, members of Washington's secondary and linebacking corps held a weekly game where, rather than playing for money, the losers had to tweet embarrassing things about themselves or flattering things about the winners.

   a. True
   b. False

3. Football Team cornerback Darrell Green returned the most interceptions for touchdowns (6) in team history. This is double the number of the six players who share

second place; however, one of those players incredibly has just three career interceptions, but he returned all three for touchdowns. Which player accomplished this feat?

a. Cornerback DeAngelo Hall
b. Linebacker Andre Collins
c. Safety Brig Owens
d. Linebacker Ryan Kerrigan

4. Although sacks are usually not a high priority for defensive backs in most coaching systems, one Washington defensive back excelled at this skill, putting up seven sacks in his Football Team career. Who?

a. Safety LaRon Landry
b. Cornerback Shawn Springs
c. Safety Brandon Meriweather
d. Safety Sean Taylor

5. The initials in popular Football Team safety D.J. Swearinger's name stand for what?

a. Dayarlo Jamal
b. David Jason
c. Donovan Jr.
d. They do not stand for anything.

6. The most solo tackles ever made by a Football Team player is 1,162. Which player accomplished this feat?

a. Linebacker Monte Coleman
b. Linebacker London Fletcher

c. Cornerback Darrell Green

d. Safety Brad Edwards

7. Safety Paul Krause came in and went out with a bang. He led the NFL in interceptions as a rookie, picking off 12 passes, and retired as the NFL's career leader with 81.

a. True

b. False

8. Which of the following is NOT a fact about talented Football Team defensive back DeAngelo Hall?

a. He once admitted to a reporter, "The way I'm playing right now, they need to cut me, because I'm not worth what I'm getting."

b. He tied the NFL record with four interceptions in one game against the Chicago Bears in 2010.

c. He owns the NFL record for most yardage gained on fumble returns.

d. He has never intercepted a pass during a postseason game.

9. Linebacker Monte Coleman played his entire career with the Washington Football Team after they snatched him in the 11th round of the 1979 NFL Draft. How long did that career last?

a. 9 years

b. 13 years

c. 16 years

d. 18 years

10. Washington cornerback Kendall Fuller recorded his first two Football Team interceptions against which two former Heisman Trophy quarterbacks?

    a. Cam Newton and Marcus Mariota
    b. Lamar Jackson and Robert Griffin III
    c. Johnny Manziel and Baker Mayfield
    d. Kyler Murray and Jameis Winston

11. Football Team mainstay Pat Fischer played over 130 NFL games with the club. Where does he rank in games played all-time for Washington?

    a. 6th overall
    b. 14th overall
    c. 37th overall
    d. 50th overall

12. Years after his playing career was over, Washington linebacker LaVar Arrington developed a sports agency and a football training system and became a broadcaster on both television and radio.

    a. True
    b. False

13. Which of the following popular television shows has outgoing Football Team cornerback Deion Sanders NOT appeared on after retiring from his playing career?

    a. Lip Sync Battle
    b. Running Wild with Bear Grylls
    c. Tiny House Nation
    d. Breaking Bad

14. Which of these current Football Team defensive backs has been with the team for four seasons, the longest current tenure in Washington's defensive backs group?

    a. Cornerback Ronald Darby
    b. Cornerback Fabian Moreau
    c. Safety Troy Apke
    d. Safety Kamren Curl

15. Which of the following statements about Football Team safety LaRon Landry is NOT true?

    a. After injuring his Achilles tendon, he opted for stem cell therapy rather than surgery, partially leading to his exit from Washington.
    b. He owned a pet monkey that went by the name of "Gucci."
    c. He combined with free safety Sean Taylor to form "Area 51" by adding their two jersey numbers (21 and 30).
    d. He won a Football Team bench press competition, besting some linemen who weighed over 100 pounds more than him.

16. In his Hall of Fame career, Washington cornerback Champ Bailey set the NFL records for most passes defended, with 203, and most Pro Bowl nominations for a defensive back, with 12.

    a. True
    b. False

17. Which of the following is NOT a fact about Washington Hall of Fame linebacker Sam Huff?

    a. He grew up in a house with no running water in a coal mining town where his father and brothers worked.

    b. He not only played for Washington but also scouted and coached for the team while he was still playing.

    c. He bred horses, including one named "Big Hitter" that ran in the Kentucky Derby.

    d. He campaigned for the U.S. House of Representatives as a Democratic Party member.

18. In 2007, promising Football Team free safety and fan favorite Sean Taylor was shot to death in his home in which city, after confronting burglars who had broken in?

    a. Washington, D.C.

    b. Miami, Florida

    c. Los Angeles, California

    d. Chicago, Illinois

19. Which of the following awards did linebacker London Fletcher NOT win during his tenure with Washington?

    a. The Bart Starr Award for character and leadership in the community

    b. The Football Team Defensive Player of the Year Award

    c. The B.J. Blanchard Award for being helpful to local reporters

    d. The Walter Payton Man of the Year Award

20. Star Washington linebacker LaVar Arrington was chosen 2nd overall in the 2000 NFL Draft but never played in the NFL again after a devastating set of injuries suffered in a 2007 motorcycle crash.

    a. True
    b. False

QUIZ ANSWERS

1. C – Darrell Green

2. B – False

3. D – Linebacker Ryan Kerrigan

4. B – Cornerback Shawn Springs

5. A – Dayarlo Jamal

6. C – Cornerback Darrell Green

7. A – True

8. D – He has never intercepted a pass during a postseason game.

9. C – 16 years

10. B – Lamar Jackson and Robert Griffin III

11. C – 37th overall

12. A – True

13. D – *Breaking Bad*

14. B – Cornerback Fabian Moreau

15. D – He won a Football Team bench press competition, besting some linemen who weighed over 100 pounds more than him.

16. A – True

17. C – He bred horses, including one named "Big Hitter" that ran in the Kentucky Derby.

18. B – Miami, Florida

19. D – The Walter Payton Man of the Year Award

20. A – True

DID YOU KNOW?

1. Passes defended is a stat that the NFL began using at the turn of the century. Cornerbacks have dominated the statistic for the Football Team, occupying the five top spots on Washington's list. Champ Bailey edges out DeAngelo Hall for the top spot, 81-80.

2. Sixteen years is a long time to play in the NFL. Linebacker Monte Coleman spent that many seasons making tackles for the Washington Football Team from 1979 to 1994 and never played a down for another team. Among linebackers, only Hall-of-Famer Ray Lewis of the Baltimore Ravens played longer (17 seasons) with a single franchise.

3. Cornerback Darrell Green bested even Coleman's feat, patrolling the backfield for Washington for 20 NFL seasons, from 1983 to 2002. Green holds the NFL record for a defensive player staying with one squad, tied with Los Angeles/St. Louis Rams offensive tackle Jackie Slater for longest overall stint by a non-kicker, and is just one season behind two kickers who hold the overall NFL record of 21 seasons (Jason Hanson of the Detroit Lions and Lou Groza of the Cleveland Browns).

4. Washington defensive back Deion Sanders was remarkably fast and effective. Opposing player Ray Horton once said of him, "I think Deion really did revolutionize the man-to-man football game of taking half the field away. What he

did, in essence, was, if you threw the ball his way, he would outrun the ball."

5. Linebacker Monte Coleman played in 215 games for the Football Team, from 1979 to 1994. He came agonizingly close to recording 1,000 solo tackles with the club, finishing with 999.

6. Cornerback DeAngelo Hall fulfilled a dream while playing for the Football Team in 2013 when he was joined in Washington by defensive end Darryl Tapp. Hall and Tapp had been childhood friends and played football together in elementary school, at Deep Creek High School, and at Virginia Tech University.

7. Five defensive backs who played for the Football Team have been enshrined in the Football Hall of Fame, although this includes two-way player Sammy Baugh, who was more famous as a quarterback. The most recent was Deion Sanders, who was elected in 2011.

8. Durability was a cornerstone of Washington linebacker London Fletcher's value. Fletcher played in the NFL from 1998 to 2013 and never missed a game. He started 215 games in a row, setting a record for linebackers and leaving him tied for sixth overall among players at any position.

9. Strong safety D.J. Swearinger was so well respected that he was voted Washington's defensive captain in 2017 despite having just signed with the team during the offseason.

10. The always unique Deion Sanders was not just a shutdown cornerback for the Football Team. He also played Major League Baseball, appearing in both the Super Bowl and the World Series. Sanders demonstrated his impact in many ways and once scored a touchdown and hit a home run in the same week.

CHAPTER 9:

WHERE'D THEY COME FROM?

QUIZ TIME!

1. Where was legendary Football Team running back John Riggins born?

    a. Plano, Texas

    b. Rochester, New York

    c. Boise, Idaho

    d. Seneca, Kansas

2. Football Team cornerback Fred Smoot, who played seven years with the team, was born and raised in Washington, D.C.

    a. True

    b. False

3. Which the following is NOT an actual college that Washington chose a player from during the 1952 NFL Draft?

    a. Elon University

    b. Case Western Reserve University

c. Southern Nantel University

d. Hardin-Simmons University

4. Which of the following superstars has NOT been involved in a trade between the Football Team and Philadelphia Eagles?

   a. Quarterback Sonny Jurgensen
   b. Quarterback Donovan McNabb
   c. Quarterback Norm Snead
   d. Running back Ricky Watters

5. From which team did the Football Team acquire useful defensive tackle Dan Wilkinson, a former 1st overall draft pick, in a 1998 swap?

   a. Detroit Lions
   b. Cincinnati Bengals
   c. New York Jets
   d. Tampa Bay Buccaneers

6. The Football Team got a fantastic deal when they dealt away a draft pick in 1999 that the New Orleans Saints used to take running back Ricky Williams. How many draft picks did they receive in return?

   a. 6 in 1999 and 2 in 2000
   b. 4 in 1999 and 3 in 2000
   c. 2 in 1999 and 4 in 2000
   d. 8 in 2000

7. The Football Team has drafted exactly the same number of players from the Michigan State Spartans and the Michigan Wolverines.

a. True

b. False

8. Which high-profile player dealt in a trade to the Football Team by the Miami Dolphins went on to be elected to the Hall of Fame?

a. Guard Dick Stanfel

b. Defensive end Bruce Smith

c. Linebacker Dave Robinson

d. Defensive end Jason Taylor

9. In one of the Football Team's best trades, wide receiver Santana Moss was acquired in exchange for fellow receiver Laveranues Coles. Which team regretted making that deal with Washington?

a. Miami Dolphins

b. New York Jets

c. Cincinnati Bengals

d. New York Giants

10. Which useful Football Team player was NOT dealt to the Houston Oilers in 1973 in exchange for Pro Bowl safety Ken Houston?

a. Defensive back Jeff Severson

b. Tight end Mack Alston

c. Linebacker Roger Goree

d. Offensive lineman Jim Snowden

11. Two players were teammates in college with the Virginia Tech Hokies in 2017 before taking the field together in Washington as well. Which two players were they?

a. Linebacker Su'a Cravens and running back Samaje Perine

b. Wide receiver Robert Davis and cornerback Fabian Moreau

c. Defensive tackle Tim Settle and cornerback Greg Stroman

d. Guard Ross Pierschbacher and running back Bryce Love

12. Washington has never in its history completed a trade with the Buffalo Bills.

a. True

b. False

13. In 2020, the Football Team traded star tackle Trent Williams to the San Francisco 49ers. Which pieces did they receive in return?

a. One 3rd round draft pick and one 5th round draft pick

b. Tackle Mike McGlinchey and one 4th round draft pick

c. Cornerback Josh Norman and one 2nd round draft pick

d. Two 2nd round draft picks

14. In 1974, the Football Team drafted kicker Mike Flater, who played for Colorado School of Mines, in the 9th round. What was his college team's nickname?

a. Coal Miners

b. Diamond Dogs

c. Mountain Men

d. Orediggers

15. Second overall pick Norm Snead played his college football as the quarterback for which program before coming to the Football Team?

    a. Memphis Tigers
    b. Syracuse Orangemen
    c. Wake Forest Demon Deacons
    d. UCLA Bruins

16. Running back Alfred Morris was acquired with a 6th round draft choice that Washington received from the Minnesota Vikings in exchange for star quarterback Donovan McNabb.

    a. True
    b. False

17. Washington running back Calvin Hill attended which prestigious Ivy League school before beginning his NFL career?

    a. Harvard University
    b. Yale University
    c. Dartmouth University
    d. Brown University

18. From which rival team did the Football Team poach star wide receiver DeSean Jackson as a free agent in 2014?

    a. New York Giants
    b. Dallas Cowboys
    c. Baltimore Ravens
    d. Philadelphia Eagles

19. The talented and flamboyant Deion Sanders was a member of which college squad before his time on the field with the Football Team?

    a. Clemson Tigers
    b. Oklahoma Sooners
    c. Florida State Seminoles
    d. Texas Longhorns

20. Washington has completed more trades with the Kansas City Chiefs than with any other NFL franchise.

    a. True
    b. False

QUIZ ANSWERS

1. D – Seneca, Kansas

2. B – False

3. C – Southern Nantel University

4. D – Running back Ricky Watters

5. B – Cincinnati Bengals

6. A – 6 in 1999 and 2 in 2000

7. A – True

8. D – Defensive end Jason Taylor

9. B – New York Jets

10. C – Linebacker Roger Goree

11. C – Defensive tackle Tim Settle and cornerback Greg Stroman

12. B – False

13. A – One 3rd round draft pick and one 5th round draft pick

14. D – Orediggers

15. C – Wake Forest Demon Deacons

16. A – True

17. B – Yale University

18. D – Philadelphia Eagles

19. C – Florida State Seminoles

20. B – False

DID YOU KNOW?

1. Football Team quarterback Mark Rypien was born in Calgary, Alberta, Canada. When Rypien won the MVP award at Super Bowl XXVI, he became the first non-American player ever to take home that distinguished honor.

2. Offensive tackle Joe Jacoby was born in Kentucky and went to college at the University of Louisville. Incredibly, the stalwart went undrafted and signed with Washington as a free agent before becoming a three-time Super Bowl champion, four-time Pro Bowler, and member of the 1980s NFL All-Decade Team.

3. The Football Team and Dallas Cowboys have had a fairly heated rivalry throughout their existence, particularly during the 1980s and 1990s. The two teams set aside their dislike for each other to make a trade at the 2014 NFL Draft, where Washington sent the 34th overall pick to Dallas, who took defensive end DeMarcus Lawrence. Washington received two later picks in return and chose Trent Murphy and Spencer Long.

4. Washington and the Philadelphia Eagles came together on a trade with major implications in 1964. Washington sent Norm Snead and Claude Crabb to the Eagles and received Jimmy Carr and star quarterback Sonny Jurgensen, who flourished for the Football Team.

5. One of the worst trades made by the Football Team occurred in 2004 when they sent defensive back Champ Bailey to the Denver Broncos with a draft pick for running back Clinton Portis. Portis was good for Washington, but at a position where the Football Team had been easily able to find good starters. Bailey remained a lockdown corner and was elected to the Hall of Fame.

6. In a decision that was heralded at the time, Washington signed free-agent defensive tackle Albert Haynesworth away from the Tennessee Titans for seven years and $100 million in 2009. However, opinion quickly soured after Haynesworth showed up out of shape, questioned the coaching scheme, and lasted just 20 games with the team. Given the size and length of the contract, some consider it the worst free-agent signing ever.

7. One of the larger and more impactful trades ever made by the Football Team was completed with the Los Angeles Rams. Washington sent seven draft picks and linebacker Marlin McKeever to Los Angeles and received six veteran players in return. Guard John Wilbur; linebackers Jack Pardee, Myron Pottios, and Maxie Baughan; defensive tackle Diron Talbert; and special teamer Jeff Jordan all came over and became the basis of the famous "Over the Hill Gang."

8. Fan favorite linebacker Monte Coleman is the only player the Football Team has ever selected from the University of Central Arkansas Bears.

9. Wide receiver Alvin Harper had an unusual NFL career in that he played on both sides of the Washington Football Team's rivalry with the Dallas Cowboys. Harper was drafted by Dallas and spent four years there. Soon after, he joined forces with Washington instead but lasted only one season with the squad before returning to Dallas to wind up his career.

10. Kicker Shaun Suisham matched Alvin Harper as well. Suisham bounced back and forth between the rivals, beginning his tenure with Dallas in 2005, signing the following year with Washington, where he found more success and stuck with the team until 2009. After being cut by the Football Team, he too re-signed with the Cowboys.

CHAPTER 10:

IN THE DRAFT ROOM

QUIZ TIME!

1. First-ever Football Team draft choice Riley Smith attended the University of Alabama, where he played for the Football Team that went by which nickname?

   a. Tigers
   b. Warriors
   c. Crimson Tide
   d. Red Raiders

2. For four consecutive years in the 1980s, the Football Team traded out of the 1st round of the NFL Draft, acquiring more proven talent in an effort to compete with the San Francisco 49ers.

   a. True
   b. False

3. From which of the following college football programs have the Football Team drafted the most players?

a. Texas Southern Tigers

b. Texas Tech Red Riders

c. Texas A&M Aggies

d. Texas-El Paso Miners

4. During the 1st round of the 2020 NFL Draft, Washington congratulated which of the following players on becoming a Football Team member remotely, via webcam, because of the COVID-19 pandemic that prevented the usual handshakes on stage?

a. Running back Antonio Gibson

b. Defensive end Chase Young

c. Quarterback Dwayne Haskins

d. Linebacker Montez Sweat

5. The Football Team selected two teammates from the Alabama Crimson Tide in the 2017 NFL Draft. Which teammates did they choose with their first two selections at the 17th and 49th overall picks?

a. Defensive end Jonathan Allen and linebacker Ryan Anderson

b. Defensive tackle Daron Payne and linebacker Shaun Dion Hamilton

c. Quarterback Dwayne Haskins and wide receiver Terry McLaurin

d. Defensive back Carlos Rogers and quarterback Jason Campbell

6. How many times in history has Washington used a top-10 overall draft pick?

a. 18

b. 29

c. 36

d. 43

7. The Football Team has never held the 1st overall pick in the NFL Draft in the entire history of the franchise.

a. True

b. False

8. Wide receiver Jamison Crowder was drafted by the Football Team in 2015 out of which school that is better known as a basketball powerhouse than a football school?

a. University of North Carolina

b. Gonzaga University

c. Duke University

d. University of Kentucky

9. Popular linebacker LaVar Arrington was drafted by Washington 2nd overall in the 2000 NFL Entry Draft. Which Hall of Fame linebacker was selected seven spots after him?

a. Brian Urlacher by the Chicago Bears

b. Ray Lewis by the Baltimore Ravens

c. Kevin Greene by the Pittsburgh Steelers

d. Junior Seau by the San Diego Chargers

10. In the 1994 NFL Draft, Washington selected two quarterbacks. Who did they take to attempt to lock down the position?

a. Cary Conklin in the 4th round and Stan Humphries in the 6th round

b. Trent Green in the 2nd round and Todd Husak in the 5th round

c. Rich Gannon in the 3rd round and Chris Hakel in the 4th round

d. Heath Shuler in the 1st round and Gus Frerotte in the 7th round

11. How high did Washington select tight end Jordan Reed in the 2013 NFL Entry Draft?

a. 1st round, 6th overall

b. 2nd round, 39th overall

c. 3rd round, 85th overall

d. 7th round, 224th overall

12. Due to their longstanding rivalry with the Dallas Cowboys, Washington has never drafted a player from the University of Texas Longhorns.

a. True

b. False

13. How many draft choices did the Football Team give up to move up and select Robert Griffin III in the 2012 NFL Draft?

a. 1

b. 2

c. 3

d. 4

14. Safety Sean Taylor played three years of college ball for which program before being drafted by the Football Team?

    a. University of Miami Hurricanes
    b. University of Florida Gators
    c. Florida State University Seminoles
    d. Florida A&M University Rattlers

15. The Football Team drafted three players from the Arizona State University Sun Devils who went on to play more than 150 NFL games each. Who were these players?

    a. Defensive end Charles Mann, tackle George Starke, and center Buzz Nutter
    b. Defensive end Kenard Lang, guard Mark Schlereth, and quarterback Norm Snead
    c. Tight end Jerry Smith, wide receiver Charley Taylor, and linebacker Derek Smith
    d. Quarterback Charlie Conerly, center Len Hauss, and wide receiver Art Monk

16. Hall of Fame cornerback Champ Bailey was such a talented athlete coming out of college that he was drafted in three sports (basketball, baseball, and football).

    a. True
    b. False

17. Which teams did the Football Team trade up with so they could select linebacker LaVar Arrington and tackle Chris Samuels 2nd and 3rd overall at the NFL Draft in 2000?

a. New Orleans Saints and San Francisco 49ers

b. Atlanta Falcons and New York Giants

c. New England Patriots and Seattle Seahawks

d. Miami Dolphins and Philadelphia Eagles

18. In 2017, Washington began a four-year run of choosing a defensive lineman with their 1st round draft selection. Which of the following players was NOT one of those four picks?

a. Defensive tackle Daron Payne

b. Defensive end Chase Young

c. Defensive end Montez Sweat

d. Defensive end Ryan Kerrigan

19. Who did the Washington Football Team select with the 1st round draft pick acquired by the team from the Rams in 2012?

a. Linebacker Ryan Kerrigan

b. Linebacker Brian Orakpo

c. Offensive tackle Trent Williams

d. Quarterback Robert Griffin III

20. From 2009 to 2012, Washington enjoyed a stretch in which they selected at least one player per year who lasted 100 games in the NFL.

a. True

b. False

QUIZ ANSWERS

1. C – Crimson Tide

2. B – False

3. C – Texas A&M Aggies

4. B – Defensive end Chase Young

5. A – Defensive end Jonathan Allen and linebacker Ryan Anderson

6. D – 43

7. B – False

8. C – Duke University

9. A – Brian Urlacher by the Chicago Bears

10. D – Heath Shuler in the 1st round and Gus Frerotte in the 7th round

11. C – 3rd round, 85th overall

12. B – False

13. D – 4

14. A – University of Miami Hurricanes

15. C – Tight end Jerry Smith, wide receiver Charley Taylor, and linebacker Derek Smith

16. B – False

17. A – New Orleans Saints and San Francisco 49ers

18. D – Defensive end Ryan Kerrigan

19. D – Quarterback Robert Griffin III

20. A – True

DID YOU KNOW?

1. In 2012, the Football Team was seeking a franchise quarterback and traded three 1st round draft choices and a 2nd round pick to the Rams for the 2nd overall pick in the draft. Washington selected Heisman Trophy winner Robert Griffin III. However, the team also selected quarterback Kirk Cousins in the 4th round of that draft, and Cousins went on to best Griffin in almost every passing statistic during the duo's time in Washington.

2. The most players Washington has drafted from any school is 34. This mark is held by the University of Notre Dame, which narrowly edges out the University of Southern California and the University of Alabama.

3. Washington has held two picks 11 times, more than any other spots in the draft. Numbers 38 and 148 are the franchise's most popular spots.

4. Washington has made four Alabama Crimson Tide players top-10 picks in the NFL Draft. The team selected linebacker Riley Smith 2nd overall in 1936, quarterback Harry Gilmer 1st overall and fullback Lowell Tew 4th overall in 1948, and tackle Chris Samuels 3rd overall in 2009.

5. In the early years, the Football Team had a habit of drafting teammates from the same college with back-to-back draft

picks. They plucked players in 1937 from the University of Washington, 1940 from Tulane University, 1941 from San Jose State University, 1942 from Duquesne University, and in 1943, they took three players consecutively from Notre Dame University.

6. Washington has drafted precisely 10 players who have played just a single game in the NFL. That number could be lowered to nine because tackle Saahdiq Charles was selected in 2020 and will likely play more games in the future.

7. Of the draft spots in the top 10 in the NFL Draft, Washington has selected at 4th overall more than any other, choosing nine players in that position. The three best among them were probably offensive tackle Trent Williams and wide receivers Michael Westbrook and Desmond Howard.

8. The smallest draft class ever selected by the Football Team in the NFL Entry Draft came in 2003 when they took just three players: wide receiver Taylor Jacobs, guard Derrick Dockery, and quarterback Gibran Hamdan.

9. The largest Football Team draft classes ever were selected in 1948, 1951, and 1959, when the team drafted 31 players over the course of the draft. About one-third of those players (34) suited up in the NFL.

10. The latest pick the Football Team has made in the NFL Draft was defensive back Chuck Willis from the University of Oregon, whom the team chose 476th overall in 1976.

Willis never made it to the NFL. Defensive tackle Frank Bosch, the team's 446th overall pick from the University of Colorado in 1968, was the latest pick they've made who played for the team.

CHAPTER 11:

COACHES, GMS, & OWNERS

QUIZ TIME!

1. Who served as the Football Team's first general manager?

    a. Dick McCann

    b. Bill McPeak

    c. George Preston Marshall

    d. Jack Espey

2. Washington general manager Bruce Allen once proposed a deal to the New England Patriots that would have sent Football Team icon Darrell Green to Massachusetts in exchange for a young and then little-known Tom Brady.

    a. True

    b. False

3. The Football Team's first head coach, Lud Wray, lasted for how long in that position with the franchise?

    a. 3 games

    b. 1 season

c. 3 seasons

d. 10 seasons

4. The Football Team's popular head coach, Joe Gibbs, won his 100th NFL game against which other team?

a. New York Giants

b. San Diego Chargers

c. Atlanta Falcons

d. Indianapolis Colts

5. Who has owned the Washington Football Team for the longest time?

a. George Preston Marshall

b. Jack Kent Cooke

c. Daniel Snyder

d. Edward Bennett Williams

6. Of all the Washington bench bosses who have coached over 50 NFL games with the team, which one had the lowest winning percentage at only .313?

a. Mike Shanahan

b. Joe Kuharich

c. Norv Turner

d. Bill McPeak

7. Washington is the only NFL franchise to have a player rise from playing for the team to ownership of the team.

a. True

b. False

8. Which coach led the Football Team to its first NFL championship?

   a. Ray Flaherty
   b. Dudley DeGroot
   c. George Allen
   d. Joe Gibbs

9. Which of the following Washington general managers once took the field as a player (though not with the Football Team) before getting the chance to guide a franchise from the front office?

   a. Mike Shanahan
   b. Scott McCloughan
   c. Otto Graham
   d. Charley Casserly

10. Who is the Washington leader in all-time coaching wins with the franchise?

    a. Jack Pardee
    b. George Allen
    c. Norv Turner
    d. Joe Gibbs

11. The most successful ownership term for a Washington Football Team owner is held by Jack Kent Cooke. How many titles did the team win while he owned the team?

    a. 2
    b. 3
    c. 4
    d. 5

12. Coach Ray Flaherty's 1942 season is the benchmark for winning percentage, as he led the team to a .909 winning percentage in the regular season.

    a. True
    b. False

13. Which of the following relatives of a famous NFL coach is NOT currently employed by the Washington Football Team?

    a. Jack Del Rio's son Luke Del Rio
    b. Joe Gibbs's grandson Peter Gibbs
    c. Norv Turner's son Scott Turner
    d. Ron Rivera's nephew Vincent Rivera

14. Two Football Team general managers have led the franchise to five playoff appearances. Which two were they?

    a. Marty Schottenheimer and Bruce Allen
    b. Dick McCann and Mike Shanahan
    c. George Allen and Bobby Beathard
    d. Otto Graham and Vinny Cerrato

15. Out of seven seasons coaching the Football Team, how many times did coach George Allen finish above .500?

    a. 2
    b. 4
    c. 5
    d. 7

16. At one point in their history, the Football Team employed four coaches over a decade who had all started for Washington at some point during their playing careers.

    a. True
    b. False

17. How did John Kent Cooke become the majority owner of the Football Team in 1997?

    a. He purchased the team when the previous owners wished to sell.
    b. He inherited the team when his father passed away due to heart failure.
    c. He forced a takeover of the corporation that had previously owned the team.
    d. He was hired as CEO of the company that owned the team.

18. How many head coaches have roamed the sidelines for the Football Team in their history?

    a. 15
    b. 20
    c. 25
    d. 30

19. Which Football Team coach won an award as the league's top coach two seasons in a row while behind the bench for Washington?

    a. George Allen
    b. Steve Spurrier

c. Joe Gibbs

d. Mike Shanahan

20. Football Team owner Dan Snyder once proposed trading franchises with New York Yankees owner George Steinbrenner as part of a business deal.

a. True

b. False

QUIZ ANSWERS

1. D – Jack Espey

2. B – False

3. B – 1 season

4. B – San Diego Chargers

5. A – George Preston Marshall

6. D – Bill McPeak

7. B – False

8. A – Ray Flaherty

9. C – Otto Graham

10. D – Joe Gibbs

11. B – 3

12. A – True

13. B – Joe Gibbs's grandson Peter Gibbs

14. C – George Allen and Bobby Beathard

15. D – 7

16. B – False

17. B – He inherited the team when his father passed away due to heart failure.

18. D – 30

19. C – Joe Gibbs

20. B – False

DID YOU KNOW?

1. Football Team coach Vince Lombardi noticed all kinds of details. Once, he saw that running back Larry Brown watched for linemen to move rather than kicking into gear at the sound of the snap count. Lombardi sent Brown for some hearing tests, then petitioned the NFL to allow an earpiece in Brown's helmet. Brown went on to make four Pro Bowls.

2. Seven men have served as both coach and general manager (or a similarly titled position) of the Washington Football Team. This started with Bill McPeak in 1962 and continues to this day with current coach and de facto general manager Ron Rivera.

3. After retiring as coach of the Football Team in 1993, Joe Gibbs began his own organization in NASCAR, Joe Gibbs Racing, which won seven Drivers' Championships.

4. A dozen Football Team head coaches have spent their entire NFL coaching careers with Washington. This number included eight of Washington's first 10 coaches, but more recent names include Steve Spurrier, Jim Zorn, and Jay Gruden.

5. Washington head coach Vince Lombardi never had a losing record in the NFL. His greatness was recognized as

the Super Bowl trophy was named after him, and he was inducted into the Hall of Fame in 1971.

6. Only one owner of the Football Team was born outside of the United States. That was Jack Kent Cooke, owner of the team from 1969 to 1996, who was born in Hamilton, Ontario, Canada.

7. In 1994, Washington swallowed its pride and hired Norv Turner as its head coach. Turner had been the offensive coordinator of the hated division rival Dallas Cowboys. Turner was a success, though, lasting several seasons with the Football Team.

8. The Football Team has never had a head coach who was born outside the United States. They have also never had a coach who was born in Washington, D.C.

9. Legendary coach Vince Lombardi took over the Football Team in 1969 and led the club to its best record in 15 years. Sadly, Lombardi passed away the day before the 1970 season began.

10. Twice in league history, a Washington general manager has been awarded the *Sporting News* NFL Executive of the Year Award. Bobby Beathard received the honor in both 1982 and 1983, making him the first person to win the award in back-to-back seasons.

CHAPTER 12:

ODDS & ENDS

QUIZ TIME!

1. Which Football Team player has won the most league MVP trophies while playing for Washington?

    a. Running back John Riggins

    b. Cornerback Darrell Green

    c. Quarterback Joe Theismann

    d. Quarterback Kirk Cousins

2. The first Football Team player to win the *Sporting News* NFL Player of the Year Award was kicker Mark Moseley in 1982.

    a. True

    b. False

3. During which season did the Football Team win their first Vince Lombardi Trophy as Super Bowl champions?

    a. 1974

    b. 1980

c. 1982

d. 1988

4. In 2019, the NFL announced its All-Time Team, recognizing the 100 greatest players from the first 100 years of NFL history. How many of these players suited up for the Football Team?

   a. 2

   b. 4

   c. 5

   d. 7

5. What negative event befell running back John Riggins before he returned to the Football Team and won the 1978 Comeback Player of the Year Award?

   a. A concussion

   b. A knee injury

   c. A cancer diagnosis

   d. A second-degree burn

6. What is Larry Michael's connection to the Washington Football Team?

   a. An architect who designed and built FedEx Field for the Football Team

   b. A beloved groundskeeper who has worked for the Football Team since 1978

   c. A player agent who represented Kirk Cousins, Pierre Garcon, and several others

d. A longtime radio announcer for the Football Team on their home station

7. The Washington Football Team has the most wins of any franchise in NFL history.

   a. True
   b. False

8. Quarterback and Football Team draft pick Robert Griffin III won the Heisman Trophy while playing for which college program?

   a. Baylor Bears
   b. Miami Hurricanes
   c. Oklahoma Sooners
   d. Washington Huskies

9. No Football Team player has ever won the NFL's Defensive Player of the Year Award while with Washington, but three players who spent time in Washington took home that trophy with other teams. Which of the following did NOT?

   a. Defensive end Bruce Smith with the Buffalo Bills
   b. Defensive end Jason Taylor with the Miami Dolphins
   c. Linebacker London Fletcher with the Buffalo Bills
   d. Cornerback Deion Sanders with the San Francisco 49ers

10. Which Football Team kicker (with at least 50 kicks attempted) holds the team's highest field goal percentage, at 87% made?

   a. Kai Forbath
   b. Mark Moseley

c. Dustin Hopkins

d. Chip Lohmiller

11. Linebacker Matt Millen was a member of the 1991 championship team in Washington but also won NFL championships with which two other franchises?

    a. Detroit Lions and Chicago Bears

    b. Green Bay Packers and Los Angeles/St. Louis Rams

    c. Pittsburgh Steelers and Miami Dolphins

    d. San Francisco 49ers and Oakland/Los Angeles Raiders

12. Washington was the first NFL team to win the Super Bowl after losing the previous year.

    a. True

    b. False

13. What is the most points the Football Team has scored in any Super Bowl?

    a. 27

    b. 37

    c. 42

    d. 53

14. Of the Football Team players in the Football Hall of Fame, Wayne Millner is the first among them to play with the Football Team. What year did he begin playing with the team?

    a. 1932

    b. 1936

    c. 1938

    d. 1941

15. Only two Football Team players have ever been named the NFL's Offensive Player of the Year. Who received that honor?

   a. Quarterback Mark Rypien and running back Clinton Portis
   b. Quarterback Sammy Baugh and wide receiver Art Monk
   c. Running back Larry Brown and quarterback Joe Theismann
   d. Quarterback Sonny Jurgensen and running back Alfred Morris

16. Kicker Mark Moseley has *missed* more field goals during his Football Team career than any other Washington player has even *attempted*.

   a. True
   b. False

17. Who was the Football Team's first Super Bowl MVP?

   a. Quarterback Doug Williams
   b. Running back John Riggins
   c. Wide receiver Gary Clark
   d. Quarterback Mark Rypien

18. Which team has faced the Football Team the most times in the Super Bowl?

   a. Buffalo Bills
   b. Los Angeles Raiders
   c. Denver Broncos
   d. Miami Dolphins

19. In which state has the Football Team competed in the most Super Bowls?

   a. Florida
   b. California
   c. Louisiana
   d. Texas

20. The Football Team is undefeated in Super Bowl games that were played in a domed stadium.

   a. True
   b. False

QUIZ ANSWERS

1. C – Quarterback Joe Theismann

2. A – True

3. C – 1982

4. D – 7

5. B – A knee injury

6. D – A longtime radio announcer for the Football Team on their home station

7. B – False

8. A – Baylor Bears

9. C – Linebacker London Fletcher with the Buffalo Bills

10. A – Kai Forbath

11. D – San Francisco 49ers and Oakland/Los Angeles Raiders

12. B – False

13. C – 42

14. B – 1936

15. C – Running back Larry Brown and quarterback Joe Theismann

16. B – False

17. B – Running back John Riggins

18. D – Miami Dolphins

19. B – California

20. A – True

DID YOU KNOW?

1. Two Football Team players have won the NFL's Walter Payton Man of the Year Award: quarterback Joe Theismann in 1982 and cornerback Darrell Green in 1996.

2. The Football Team players who have earned the most career Pro Bowl invitations are both defensive backs. Champ Bailey and Ken Houston both were selected a dozen times.

3. Football Team icon Adrian Peterson ranks fifth on the all-time list for most rushing yards in the NFL, behind legends Emmitt Smith, Walter Payton, Frank Gore, and Barry Sanders.

4. Two Washington players have been named the NFL's Offensive Rookie of the Year. In 1975, running back Mike Thomas was selected, and quarterback Robert Griffin III won the 2012 award with his electrifying play.

5. In 1983, 32 years after it had last happened, two Washington players finished first and second in NFL scoring for the season. Kicker Mark Moseley finished first, with 161 points, and was followed closely by running back John Riggins with 144.

6. The Football Team's value is estimated at $3.4 billion by *Forbes* magazine, which ranks them as the seventh most valuable NFL team and 14th in any sport around the globe.

7. Coach Joe Gibbs is the only man to have two stints at the helm of the Football Team. Gibbs coached them from 1981 to 1992 and returned more than a decade later in 2004. His second term was less successful, and Gibbs was gone after 2007.

8. When the team left Robert F. Kennedy Stadium, many in Washington were sad to see it go. This was not necessarily due to the charm of the stadium, but because the Football Team went 173-102-3 during its time there and was 11-1 in playoff games at RFK.

9. In the 1987 NFL season, when players went on strike, the league still held games with replacement players stepping in. Washington was the only franchise without a single player stepping across the picket line.

10. Only one Football Team player has won the NFL's Defensive Rookie of the Year Award, but he is the most recent: Defensive end Chase Young took home the title in 2020.

CONCLUSION

There you have it, an amazing collection of Washington Football Team trivia, information, and statistics at your fingertips! Regardless of how you fared on the quizzes, we hope that you found this book entertaining, enlightening, and educational.

Ideally, you knew many of these details but also learned a good deal more about the history of the Washington Football Team, its players, coaches, management, and some of the quirky stories surrounding the team. If you got a little peek into the colorful details that make being a fan so much more enjoyable, then mission accomplished!

The good news is that the trivia doesn't have to stop there! Spread the word. Challenge your fellow Football Team fans to see if they can do any better. Share some of the stories with the next generation to help them become Washington supporters too.

If you are a big enough Football Team fan, consider creating your own quiz with some of the details you know that weren't presented here and then test your friends to see if they can match your knowledge.

The Washington Football Team is a storied franchise. They have a long history with multiple periods of success and a few that were less than successful. They've had glorious superstars, iconic moments, hilarious tales...but most of all, they have wonderful, passionate fans. Thank you for being one of them.

Made in the USA
Middletown, DE
08 December 2024

66433955R10080